PANDA

BACK FROM THE BRINK

ZHOU MENGQI

Contributing editor

MICHAEL KERRIGAN

Introduction by

IAIN VALENTINE

Science consultants

HU JINCHU, ZHANG HEMIN, ZHANG ZHIHE

Adapted from *China's Giant Panda* 中国大熊猫
Copyright © 2010 by Sichuan Fine Arts Publishing House Co., Ltd., China
Photography by Zhou Mengqi
China's Giant Panda originally published in Chinese
is published by Sichuan Fine Arts Publishing House Co., Ltd. in 2010

Saraband 🌀

Above: Named for the village of Lufeng, in southern China's Yunnan province, where its fossil remains were unearthed, *Ailurarctos lufengensis* flourished approximately 8 million years ago.

Above: Much of what we know about the evolution of the panda has been pieced together from fragmentary finds. These overdeveloped molars couldn't belong to any other beast.

Opposite: The red panda is not closely related to the giant panda, but favours a diet of bamboo, like its namesake.

AN INADEQUATE DIET?

The fact that it's only partially successful in digesting bamboo explains the long hours (up to fourteen daily) that the panda has to spend browsing, the amount that it eats (up to 38kg), and the comparative listlessness that it nevertheless exhibits. Pandas are slow and sparing in their movements, and economic in their expenditure of energy; only as cubs do they exert themselves unnecessarily. It would be wrong to assume that the panda's diet is inadequate – after all, bamboo has sustained the panda perfectly well over millions of years – but it's certainly correct to say that the panda ekes out its life on a very narrow nutritional margin, and that its lifestyle is limited as a result.

We've grown accustomed to the idea that animals evolve in order to be perfectly adapted to their environments. Although it may be true, aspects of that adaptation may also be influenced by behavioural factors. Being a panda is partly about being big and bear-like, black-and-white and furry, but it's also about eating, sleeping and not doing too much else.

AN EVOLUTIONARY ABERRATION?

There's no doubt that the panda lives very differently from most other mammals, and that what suits other species wouldn't suit the panda, and vice versa. But the argument that this makes it some sort of evolutionary freak is very much mistaken. For whatever its apparent limitations, the panda has survived for several million years.

It's worth remembering that *Hominidae*, the family of hominids to which humans (*Homo sapiens*) belong, emerged at most only 7 million years ago – in other words, some time after *Ailurarctos lufengensis* (see page 13). 'Lucy' – the *Australopithecus* female found in the East African Rift Valley, and a fairly distant human ancestor – didn't walk the earth until just over 3 million years ago. And *Homo sapiens,* in its present form, is believed to have existed for only some 200,000 years, so we're hardly in a position to judge the panda's pedigree!

If the giant panda is endangered, that's not because it's been wasting away, weakened by malnutrition (or, for that matter, dying out due to some supposed problem with reproduction). The idea of the 'Darwinian' struggle, of the 'survival of the fittest', is much misunderstood, but there's no doubt that if the panda hadn't been equipped to survive, it would not be here now. That doesn't mean that it's invulnerable, though. Like other species the world over, the panda population has taken a hammering in recent centuries as its habitats have been inexorably cleared for human settlement and agricultural development, thereby pushing the panda to the mountainous margins of its Chinese homeland.

RED PANDA, RED HERRING?

The red panda (*Ailurus fulgens*) is nothing like as close in kinship to the giant panda as its name implies. Indeed, *Ailurus fulgens* belongs to its own family, the *Ailuridae*, which is entirely separate from the *Ursidae* family, to which the giant panda, *Ailuropoda melanoleuca*, belongs.

Both species are members of the *Carnivora* order, however, and, within that, of the *Caniformia* (or 'dog-like') sub-order, so they are related to that extent. But given that the *Caniformia* includes everything from the *Canidae* (wolves, foxes, jackals, dogs and others) through the *Mustelidae* (among which are counted mink and otters) to the *Pinnipedia* (which includes sea lions and seals), we can see that related species may vary enormously. *Ailurus fulgens* is far smaller than *Ailuropoda melanoleuca*, and it is raccoon-like not only in size, but in its similar head shape and stripy tail. Altogether, it bears very little resemblance to the giant panda.

Yet despite their differences in shape and stature, there are similarities between the red and giant pandas as well, which explains why the idea of their kinship was taken seriously for so long. Some of the resemblances are superficial, such as their thick fur and engaging eye-patches and an overlapping area of distribution (although the red panda's range extends further to the west, into the Himalayas). More intriguingly, though, the two species share the same curious status in being overwhelmingly non-carnivorous carnivores, for like its giant namesake, the red panda lives largely on bamboo. In addition, it has evolved a version of the giant panda's radial sesamoid 'thumb' (see page 14).

Above: Pandas hold food with their special 'thumb' and chew
through the tough stems with their strong molar teeth.

A PRESTIGIOUS PRIZE

TIMES CHANGE, AND SO DO PERCEPTIONS. The references made to the panda in Chinese sources dating from the first millennium BC describe a very different beast from the panda that we know today – and an altogether less cuddly one. The first reference we find to the animal comes in the *Historical Record* of Sima Qian, a scholar of the Han Dynasty, who was writing during the first century BC. He describes the panda as having even more strength and ferocity than the tiger or leopard. Indomitable in war, it was an obvious emblem of the emperor's might.

PANDA PARADOX

Yet its ferocity was only half of the panda that the ancients saw. Like us, they were very much taken by the animal's air of quiet introspection, even if they didn't see its placid nature as evidence of docility or warmth, but as stoic dignity. What we imagine to be gentleness was instead regarded as something akin to the supreme warrior's outward calmness.

There was more to the ancient Chinese view of the giant panda than that, though. More open, perhaps, than we are to multiplicities of meaning, and also to paradoxes, the ancient Chinese considered the panda to be a symbol of both war-like power and peace. With its huge bulk, its mighty strength, its impressive claws and its giant jaws, this bear – this carnivore – they reasoned, was well endowed with all that it needed to create murderous mayhem. Instead, however, it had opted to lead a quiet, pastoral existence as a grazing creature.

As such, it was a fitting symbol of a just and modest model ruler who has the strength to wage war, yet prefers to pursue the path of peace. This symbolic meaning gave rise to the Chinese tradition of a flag bearing the figure of a panda being raised whenever a battling army wished to call a truce. The panda stood for peace without the stigma of surrender.

IN BLACK AND WHITE

Panda skulls unearthed by archaeologists excavating the Chinese imperial tombs of the second century BC support the suggestion that these beasts were held in reverence, although exactly what sort of ceremonial or symbolic role they served is far from clear. Were they interred in the graves as treasured trophies from this life, or as talismanic guardians for the next one? Or did they fulfil some other function that we can't even begin to guess at?

Chronicles also record captive pandas in the Chinese emperor's collection. This was something like a private zoo, but seems unlikely to have been a place of research, as is its modern equivalent; more probably, pandas were kept as living good-luck charms, and as evidence of the ruler's wealth and power. This explanation seems to be the logic behind the gifts of pandas made to foreign rulers, such as the pair of living pandas that scribes of the Japanese Emperor Temmu record as being received in AD 658 from China's Empress Wu Zetian. Along with these diplomatic offerings, she also sent some seventy panda skins.

The panda's pelt, with its bold, black-and-white patterning, is an irresistible aspect of its appeal for us, as it was for the ancient Chinese. They read a mystical significance into those markings, seeing them as suggesting the interlocking colours of yin and yang, and thus all of the conflicting forces of the universe brought into harmony within a single form.

Above: The panda featured in a number of ancient Chinese texts under different names: it was described as a tapir, for example, or as a 'white', 'striped' or 'bamboo' bear.

Above, left: In the *Shan Hai Jing* (the *Collection of Mountains and Seas*, c.200 BC), the giant panda's huge jaws earned it the description 'iron-eating bear'.

Above, centre: In the *Book of History*, written around the start of the first millennium BC, the panda is seen as possessing overwhelming ferocity and a tiger's strength.

Above, right: The *Book of Changes* (c.1000 BC) confirms the panda's status as a symbol of power and imperial prestige. Its pelt was once offered to great rulers as a tribute.

Left: The buddleia was just one of many hundreds of plants recorded by Père David during his Chinese travels.

Below: Its bamboo diet is responsible for the giant panda's massive jaw and round-faced appearance.

Above: Even a hard-bitten naturalist like Père Armand David wasn't immune to the engaging appeal of the panda, a new species to him, and one that he described as being 'easily the most pretty I have come across'.

Left and above: It's hard for us to imagine anything more winningly winsome than a young panda, with its air of comic melancholy. Yet nineteenth-century naturalists had no qualms about collecting panda skins.

POPULATION PRESSURES

China went through enormous changes during what we in the West call the early modern period. Having remained relatively stable for a thousand years (at between 60 and 100 million), the country's population then rose extraordinarily steeply. In power from the end of the fourteenth century, the Ming Dynasty established relative stability and peace within the country, like its successor, the Qing Dynasty, also pushing back its boundaries by a successful policy of military expansion. While China's land area grew, its population was also increasing in leaps and bounds: by 1800, it was approaching the 400 million mark, and was climbing fast.

That such growth could be sustained is testimony to the industry and skill with which the Chinese worked their land. Higher-yielding strains of rice were developed; the use of natural fertilisers was perfected; tools were refined; and techniques of irrigation were introduced, as were previously unfamiliar crops, many (like maize, groundnuts and

yams) brought from the New World. New lands were brought under cultivation, too, by expansion from valley floors to surrounding hillsides. Forests were felled, bamboo thickets were cleared, and farmers learned how to construct terraces so that hitherto uncultivable slopes could be put into agricultural production.

Even now, China was struggling to feed its expanding population, prompting streams of migrants to set out for what had thus far been largely unsettled frontier regions. Beginning in the valleys, vast tracts of trees and bamboo were cleared here, too. Industrial development during the second half of the twentieth century only increased the pressure.

An economic miracle spelled an ecological disaster, for as the human population soared, so that of the giant panda steadily declined. By the middle of the twentieth century, *Ailuropoda melanoleuca* had become an endangered species, and experts believed that there could only be a few hundred left – maybe just over a thousand at most.

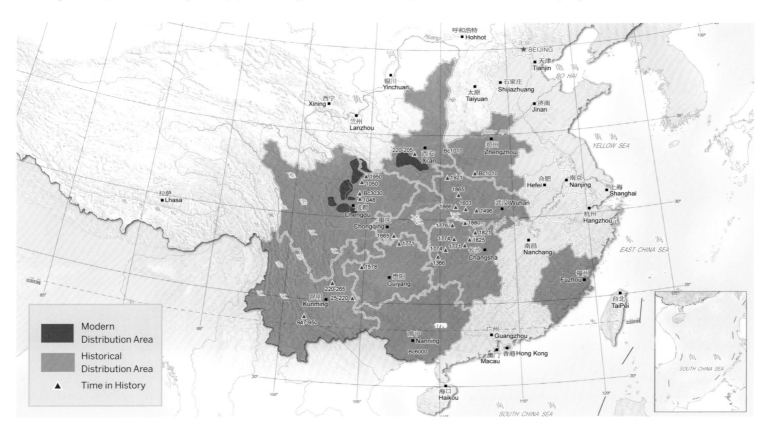

Above and opposite: Once more widespread, giant pandas are now largely restricted
by human activity, mountains and earthquakes to patches of montane forest
between 1,500 and 3,000m above sea level.

Above: Being primarily solitary, the fragmentation of suitable habitat by human activity is a serious threat to pandas finding a mate.

Opposite: As China's population grew over the centuries, so its area of settlement steadily expanded and vast areas of forest were cleared. Today, the Chinese wilderness is beautiful, but sparse.

Pages 60 and 61: A watchful panda keeps a lookout from a lofty perch. The past twenty centuries or so have seen human settlement advancing inexorably upon surviving panda strongholds.

CHAPTER TWO
A HOME IN
THE HILLS

Viewing an online map in satellite mode, it's the snowy line of the Himalayas that arrests the eye: there's a sense of energy, almost of movement. Like a dazzling white wave, the world's greatest mountain range seems to surge across the heart of Asia. To the southwest lie the scorching plains of India; to the north, an endless emptiness of arid steppe; while to the southeast, the mountains wheel around, tapering away into the land of Myanmar (Burma). To the east, subsidiary mountain ranges spill across the Tibetan Plateau and over into western China, apparently swirling, eddying and jostling one another as they go. The last big splashes on the map are the Qionglai and Qinling Mountains.

A LONER'S LIFE

THERE ARE JUST UNDER 7 BILLION PEOPLE IN THE WORLD TODAY, with approximately a fifth of them living in China. Beijing alone has almost 20 million inhabitants, whilst the municipality of Shanghai has over 23 million. It isn't just the cities that are teeming with people, though: much of China's countryside is crowded, too, with average population densities of over 700 per km² in the east.

There's no shortage of people there, then, but if China is the world's most populous nation, it's also one of the biggest in terms of its geographical extent (it's either the third- or fourth-largest in the world, depending how you make the calculation). There's room for everyone, in other words, and while it's undeniably a squeeze in the south and east, in the remoter, western regions there's space to spare. Indeed, you can walk for miles in the hill country (at least, you can if you can find a way through the thick bamboo) without seeing another soul.

TERRITORIAL RIGHTS

The relative spaciousness of this part of China is just as well, given the panda's need for room in which to graze undisturbed, and not just by human beings, but also by others of his or her own kind. The panda may not wander far, but it needs a considerable amount of space, largely because it requires the resources – the bamboo and water – that that space contains.

Its fundamental drive to secure what it needs to survive doesn't just colour the panda's approach to its life, but its attitude towards other pandas, too.

Irresistibly cute as it may appear, the panda's cuddliness is deceptive: it may look like a soft toy, but it's nothing like as companionable and unthreatening as it seems. Whether male or female, the panda is for the most part content to live entirely alone, and keeps itself to itself for months on end. Not only is the company of others not sought out, it is also actively – even aggressively – shunned. Jealously guarding its territory, which may be anything up to 7km², the panda uses much of the energy that it has left after its daily round of feeding and watering to police its boundaries. Pandas secrete a scent from a gland between the anus and the genital areas and rub their rears on rocks or the bases of trees to mark out their territory. They scratch tree trunks with their claws to proclaim their presence, too, and when climbing up trees to keep a lookout, they cry out threateningly to warn off intruders.

Right: The panda marks out its territory with its scent to warn off intruders.

Below: A young panda remains in its mother's territory for up to three years.

Left: A tender scene: pandas may be the very picture of mutual affection, yet no enduring partnership will follow from their mating.

Pages 96–97: The panda calls out threateningly to warn interlopers away from its territory.

Left: Adult pandas rarely interact with one another in the wild. When they do, it is for breeding purposes.

Right: Sometimes appearing quite comical balanced atop a branch, pandas exhibit great flexibility and agility, facilitated by the sesamoid bones in their paws (see page 14).

Pages 132–33: The panda's view is uninterrupted from its lookout post high up above the forest floor. There may well be much more warmth and sunlight up here, too.

Pages 134–35: The panda cub quickly comes to feel its safest in the trees above the earth, although it will always have to descend to ground level in order to feed.

Opposite and below: With its dense, soft fur for warmth, and its hairy-soled paws for grip, the panda is well equipped to deal with the very worst of the winter weather.

SCIENTIFIC STUDY

EXTRAORDINARY EFFORTS WERE MADE TO PROTECT THE PANDA IN ITS HOME ENVIRONMENT FROM THE EARLY 1960s, but few in China or beyond believed that conservation should stop there. Even with such support, it was clear that the animal faced a fight to survive, and that if it was to make it, humans would have to battle on its behalf. Yet how was this to be done? What help – specifically – was needed? What measures could reasonably be taken to back up this beleaguered species? The more closely naturalists considered these questions, the more conscious they became of how little was really known about the animal that they were setting out to save. And without such knowledge, their enthusiasm risked being misdirected and their strategies ineffective, and maybe even damaging. Yet it was one thing to recognise the importance of scientific study, and quite another to come up with realistic ways in which it might be pursued. The giant panda was rare not only in the sense of being few in number, but also in being unusual – indeed, unique. As we've seen (turn to pages 16–17 and 36), until recently, researchers were still vague as to what kind of animal the panda even was. Was it a bear? Or some kind of glorified raccoon? Coming up with the answers to such questions was going to be difficult, they realised, given that the panda lived so remotely and was so elusive in its habits.

PANDA CENTRAL

The opening of a designated research centre in 1980 was a huge break-through in studying the panda, even before its staff had any scientific findings to report. Situated in the heart of panda country, in Sichuan's Wolong National Nature Reserve, this Chinese government institution enjoyed the support of the World Wildlife Fund. In 1987, the research effort was redoubled with the foundation of a major new 'panda base', the Panda Breeding and Research Centre. This venture, too, was backed by the WWF. Situated in the northern suburbs of Chengdu, western Sichuan's main city, a collection of half-a-dozen pandas, rescued from

the wild, was installed here in specially designed enclosures. During the months and years that followed, scientists were able to examine them at close quarters; to monitor their behaviour, singly and in groups; and to carry out systematic tests on just about every aspect of panda physiology and health.

By 1989, research at the centre had already made such strides forward that it was given a Global 500 award by the United Nations Environment Programme (UNEP) in recognition of its right to be considered among the 500 frontline 'heroes' of global environmental action. It won the same honour again in 1994.

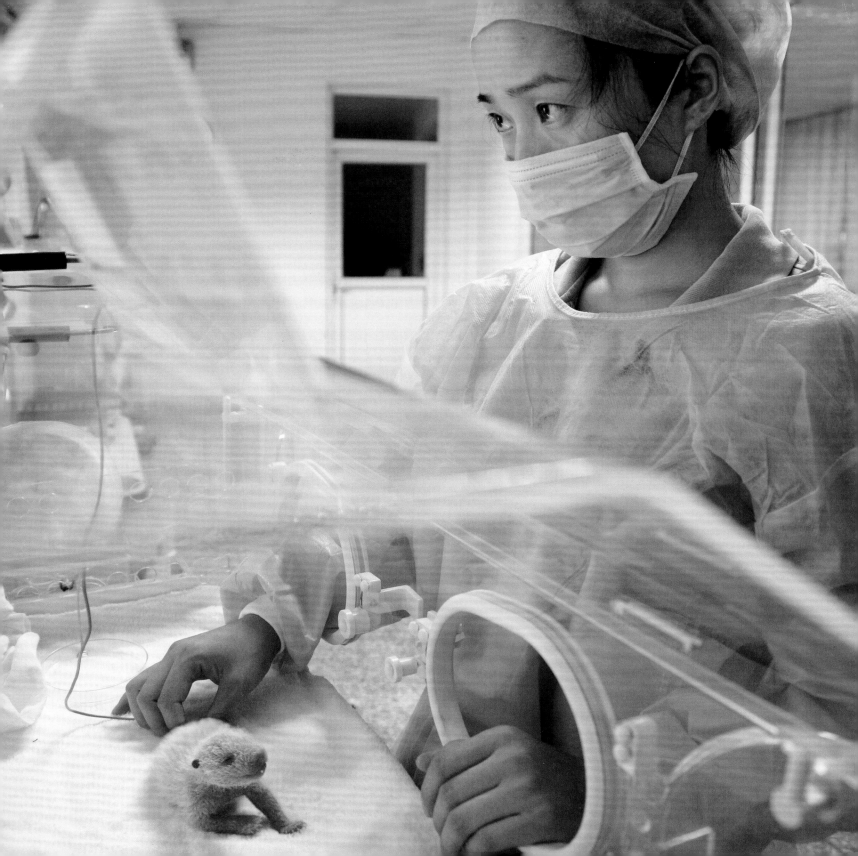

Above, opposite and pages 174–75: Members of staff at Chengdu have acquired enormous experience and expertise in every aspect of panda reproduction and early care.

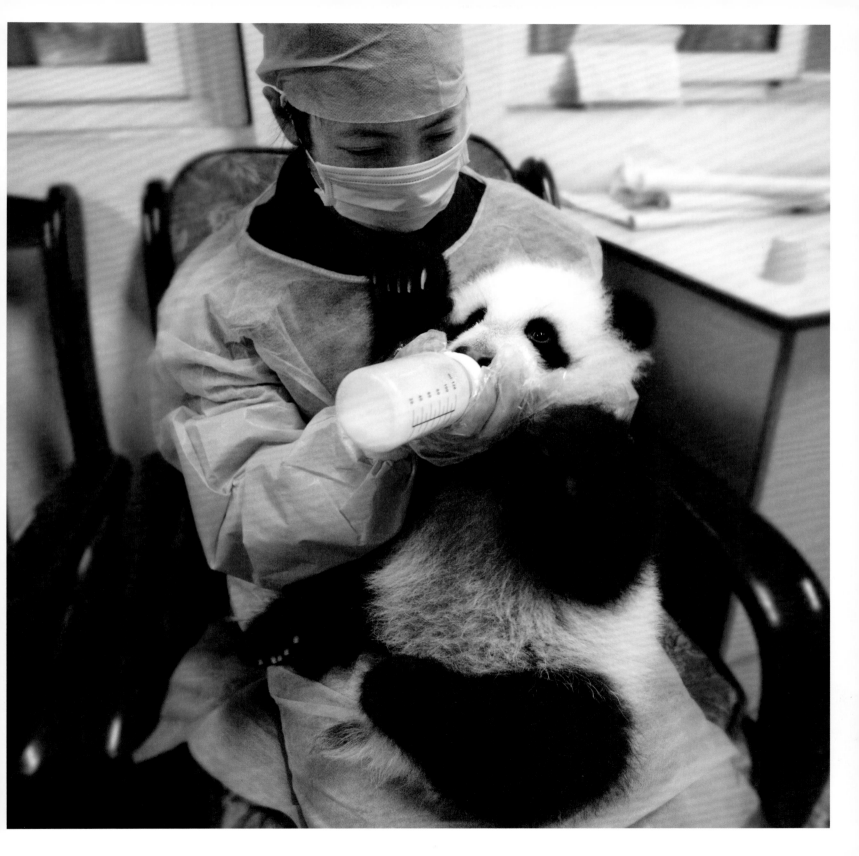

INDEX